Strawberry's Journey

To Flagstaff

Mile High
Veterinary
Clinic

3

Prescott

2 Fawn spends
first night

Pine

Strawberry

1

Fawn taken
by dog

4 Bradshaw
Mt. Wildlife
Preserve

Agua Fria
National
Monument

N

Phoenix

Tonto
National
Park

Sonoran Desert
National Monument

Ironwood Forest
National Monument

Arizona-Sonora
Desert Museum   5   Tucson

To Mexican Border

Strawberry Finds a Home

by Beverly A. Bear, © 2015
StrawberryFindsaHome@gmail.com

ISBN: 1-4276-0233-6
Child Education, Nature, Saving Animals

Strawberry's story is based on a real event. In the summer of 2002, a tiny White-tailed fawn was carried unharmed out of the forest in northern Arizona by a sheepdog-retriever named Winston. Jim Colenso, Winston's owner, heard the fawn's cries and demanded that his dog lay her down. Afraid of what his second dog, Moose, might do, Jim took the fawn to his neighbors Bess and Bud Basham. They fed the tiny fawn and contacted a park forest ranger and animal rehabilitator from the Tonto Natural Bridge State Park, Cathe Descheemacher, who rescued the baby from dehydration and hunger. She called Francois de Martini, Co-director of Bradshaw Mt. Preserve and animal worker at the Mile High Veterinary Clinic in Prescott, who agreed to take the fawn and raise her until she could be returned to the forest with others of her kind. When no other White-tailed fawns came to the preserve, it was decided that the fawn must stay. The Arizona Game and Fish Department, who have responsibility for rescued wildlife, arranged with Shawnee Riplog-Peterson, curator of Mammology and Ornithology at the Arizona Sonora Desert Museum, for the deer to become a permanent resident at the museum's facility in Tucson.

I dedicate this book to my dear husband, David,

and to all persons who love wildlife and want to preserve it

in its own natural setting.

My life begins in the wild. Sunlight dapples my spotted fur.

I look just like the forest floor. When my mother goes away

to feed each morning, she sings me a goodbye song:

Lie very still, my little girl, and do not move a hair.

You're still too young to have much smell. You're safe from Mr. Bear.

Remember when you need me, I'm not far away.

I'll come back to feed you, just stay here all day.

I sleep all afternoon where the warm

summer air smells like honey.

One morning while Mother is away, I hear bushes rustling. I smell a strange smell. A shadow falls over me. I see a yellow, four-footed animal. He jumps back and barks. My heart pounds loudly. When this animal opens his mouth wide, I am sure he means to swallow me. But he places his mouth gently on the nape of my neck and lifts me up. We move down the hill. I cry and cry.

A chaser, thief and rogue, I've been called all three, But I'm not any one of those, I'm just me!

Here's a little fawn. Hasn't moved a hair. Just lies here at dawn, giving me a stare.

Maybe she and I can play.

Hope her mother doesn't come. I'll carry her away.

Suddenly I smell another strange scent. A tall two-footed animal

runs toward us. "Winston, come here! Put that fawn down!"

He scoops me up in his arms. I breathe in a deep breath and

stop crying. "I'm taking you to meet two persons who will

help," he says. The two people feed me drops of white liquid

that smells like my mother's milk. But it's not enough.

I'm still hungry. I lick one person's neck. They call a

ranger for help.

7

The ranger arrives and takes me to her home. She prepares some milk, then puts a drop of it on her finger and offers it to me. When I lick it, she kneels on the floor and places me between her knees, saying, "Here, take this bottle." I suck and suck and fall asleep. Each time I cry during the night, she comes to feed me.

By morning, when she moves about her house, I follow her everywhere. Then she holds me very gently and says, "Since I cannot keep you here with me, I will take you to an animal shelter. When you get bigger and stronger, they plan to release you back into the forest again with other White-tailed deer."

She carries me out to the car. "I'm going to put you in this small dog

carrier to keep you safe. Before you go to the shelter we will go to

a veterinary clinic."

We drive for a long time. When we arrive at the clinic, I smell

a lot of new smells. The animal helper, who is called Francois,

puts me up on a cold surface. I shiver and my legs feel

shaky. He looks deep into my eyes and pokes at my chest.

"I believe you will live," he says.

At sunset, he puts me into another carrier. We take a

long, bumpy ride to the animal shelter, where he also

works. By now I am really tired.

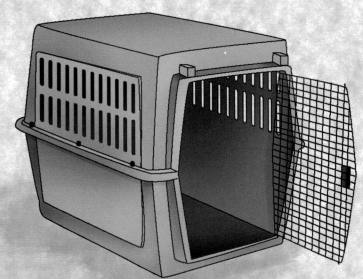

At the shelter, Francois hands me to another person, named Tracey. She holds me close to her and strokes my fur gently. She says in a soft voice. "I'm sorry that a dog carried you away from your mother and your forest home."

Tracey keeps me by myself in my carrier for a week to make sure I'm well. I know I'm not ill. I am heartbroken. I miss my mother so much, her smell and her gentle licking. Tracey comes five times a day to feed me. While she is feeding me, she says, "You need to have a name, my little one. I want to call you Strawberry after the small town where you were found."

One day Tracey says, "Today you're ready to meet the other baby deer." She leads me out to a large fenced area she calls "the nursery." "The other baby deer are called Mule deer," she tells me. "You are a White-tailed deer, Strawberry."

I see that these Mule deer are bigger than me and have larger ears. Suddenly I hear the sound of many hooves. I look up and see three baby bucks running straight toward me. My heart hammers. One rears and strikes at me. I run as fast as I can while they chase me. I cry out loudly.

We are the Bully Buck Three. We rule this nursery!

We've come to let you know that you will have to go!

Over the noise of their hooves, I hear a White-tailed mother deer calling. She runs between me and the bucks. "My name is Sedona," she says. She leads me to a shelter where I fall asleep. She takes me to drink water, and we nibble tender grasses. She teaches me many new things.

You need to rest my little deer. The tiny shed is cool and near.

I'll lie beside you and keep you safe. So you won't need to fear.

One day she says, "When you go back to the forest, you will need to know how to sniff the wind. The wind will usually be your friend except when it whirls many smells and sounds all around.

The days get shorter and the fall weather is cool. One October night I smell a strange odor on the wind. Suddenly we hear fierce shrieks. I see a mean-looking, four-footed animal moving quickly toward our nursery. Then I see a second one. The first runs up the side of our cage. He looks down at us and growls. The second one runs to the side, stands on his back legs and rattles the wire. I tremble with fear. I am certain these wild beasts will soon be inside our cage. I cry out. Even Sedona acts afraid.

"Hey, Brother," says the big cat. "Look inside that wire cage. Many little baby deer, waiting here to be our supper. You attack from this side. I'll break in from the upper."

Tracey and Francois run towards us. They wave their arms over their heads and shout and shout. "Get out of here, you cougars. Get out of here and don't come back!" The two cougars stop. Then they both run away, like wind-driven fires.

Day after day I get bigger. My spots disappear. I am old enough to go back to the forest, but I am still the only White-tailed fawn and I can't go back alone. I am very sad. I know now that I will never be able to see my mother again or go home to my pine forest.

One afternoon Tracey says, "I've talked with an animal expert named Shawnee at the Arizona-Sonora Desert Museum. She says she needs you to come live there and be a friend to their elderly White-tailed deer. She wants you because you are a young female who is comfortable with both deer and people."

I am very sad to leave Sedona and Tracey and the other deer. I take a long time to say my good-byes. I am put in a truck for my long trip to the museum. This time I ride in a big dog carrier. I'm a much larger deer now. We leave the cool mountains with many pine trees and we go down to the hot desert with many tall cactuses.

When we get to the museum, Shawnee keeps me away from the other deer. She needs to know I am well. She tells me that I will meet the other deer, named Wilma, when she is sure that I am healthy.

Finally, Shawnee leads me to a large open-air enclosure. The pine trees smell sweet. The scent reminds me of my forest home. Suddenly, the wind begins to blow. The smells and sounds of neighboring wolves, bear and cougars whirl around me. I race one way and then another. My heart pounds.

When the wind stops, I stand very still and sniff. I smell the other deer who is called Wilma. As soon as she smells and sees me, she runs right at me. I race away. She chases me. I begin to cry.

Who are you? Who are you? You need to leave.

My sister is dead. I need to grieve.

After Shawnee takes me back to my own place for the night, I decide that Wilma and I must become friends.

Next day, the first thing I do when Shawnee leads me back to the deer enclosure is walk right up to Wilma and ask, "Would you like to play?"

I don't want to play today. But since it seems you're here to stay, I'll show you where we drink and eat, and where we sleep when wild coyotes creep.

This time, instead of chasing me away, she shows me where we drink water, where we eat our tasty hay, and where we sleep. She and I grow to like each other. Soon we stand close and we lick each other.

The next day, the elder deer explains, "We have a very special job here. We are teachers. We teach museum visitors about our White-tailed kind. We show people what White-tailed deer look like, what we eat and how we play. When they meet one of us in the wild, they will know what very few do.

And now you know my story true.

I am content in my new museum home
and I would like to share with you
a simple lesson you need to learn.

If you see a fawn like me lying quietly
in the woods, remember that her mother deer
is probably grazing very near.

So just relax and let her be.
Let her stay out in the wild
with her mommy by her side.

Then she can grow up to be free.

I'm especially grateful to Mary Fergusen, friend and professional photographer, for her inspiration and encouragement to write this unusual story of how a tiny, spirited White-tailed fawn survived her challenging beginnings in 2002 and came to live permanently at the Arizona-Sonora Desert Museum in Tucson. I'm indebted to Thomas Stauffer, reporter for the Arizona Daily Star, who supplied important information. As a result, I contacted Alie Amato, owner and director, and Francois de Martini, Tracey Head, and Heather Buck, all animal care specialists at the Bradshaw Mountain Wildlife Refuge near Mayer, Arizona, who gave generously of their time and expertise in sharing their stories about the little deer's six-month stay and her experiences there.

I am especially grateful to Tracey for naming the little doe Strawberry after the little northeastern Arizona town called Strawberry, Arizona, where the fawn was found because that made it possible for me to learn the rest of the fawn's story.

I began my search at the Chamber of Commerce in Payson, Arizona, the largest town near Strawberry, where I asked if anyone remembered the story of a three- or four-day old fawn being carried in unharmed by a dog. Pat Johnson stepped forward and said she believed she did remember. She contacted Rose Harper, Strawberry resident and neighbor of the dog, Winston, and his caregiver, Jim Colenso. Rose called Jim and arranged a meeting for me with Jim and his dog on the following day. From Jim, I learned of the important role that his neighbors Bud and Bess Basham played in helping the tiny baby doe survive by feeding her goat's milk and making persistent phone calls to locate an animal care rehabilitator on Sunday. They finally located Cathe Descheemaker, ranger from the Tonto Natural Bridge State Park, who agreed to come out to rescue the fawn from dehydration and hunger. When I spoke with the Bashams and Cathe Descheemaker, they gave me invaluable details about the early hours the little fawn spent with them after Jim's dog Winston brought her in. In addition, I appreciate my meeting with Shawnee Riplog-Peterson, head mammologist and ornithologist at the Arizona-Sonora Desert Museum, who showed me the specially designed outdoor area where the doe lives and the indoor area where she sleeps. I appreciate so much the information that she shared about the characteristics and habits of these White-tailed deer and about her philosophy concerning the importance of museum visitors learning about their wild White-tailed neighbors.

In addition to all these people who helped me learn about Strawberry's story and about White-tailed deer, I am so grateful to those special people who have helped me with the actual writing, editing and revising of Strawberry's story: Carole Anderson, journalist; Eva Bear, retired grade school teacher; Jeff Caruthers, Journalism Professor at the Carleton University, Ottawa, Canada; children's book author, Judy Cox; Tresa Eyres, writer; Sara Jameson, English instructor at Oregon State University, Corvallis, Oregon, who has shepherded me through the entire book creation process; Elizabeth Keyser, Professor Emeritus of English at Hollins University in Roanoke, Virginia; Virginia Lissitz, retired kindergarten teacher; Susan Lynn-Rivera, retired children's librarian and writer; writer Juliana Sandahl; Miriam Showalter, children's writer and book editor; and Emily Wills, writer.

Special thanks go to Kim Roth, grade school teacher at St. Mary's Public School in Mt. Angel, Oregon, who took the book to several of her classrooms, read the story to her students, and shared their comments and suggestions.

Book illustrator Katherine Clark and graphic designer Sharon McKee gave generously of their time to critique the text.

I owe special thanks to my neighbor, Wayne Logon, retired animal biologist with the State of Oregon, who shared his knowledge of deer and their habits.